A Teddy Hors[le]

Hide an[d]

Teddy and Betsy know God cares for them

Based on the Parables of the Lost Sheep and the Lost Coin

by Leslie J Francis and Nicola M Slee
Pictures by Laura Cooper

The Bear facts:

The Teddy Horsley Bible Series is designed to build bridges between the young child's day-to-day experiences of the world and major biblical themes and stories.

Both authors work in church-related institutions of education. Nicola Slee is currently Visiting Scholar at The Queen's College, Birmingham. Leslie Francis is Professor of Pastoral Theology at the University of Wales, Lampeter, and Trinity College, Carmarthen. The illustrator, Laura Cooper, is a teacher and artist.

The Teddy Horsley Series is a result of extensive research into the religious development of young children, and the authors' and illustrator's wide experience of educational work in schools and churches.

Published by:
National Christian Education Council
1020 Bristol Road
Selly Oak
Birmingham
B29 6LB

British Library Cataloguing in Publication Data:
A catalogue record for this book is available from
the British Library.

Text © Leslie J Francis and Nicola M Slee 1998
Illustrations © Laura Cooper 1998

Unless otherwise stated, quotations from the Bible are from the *Good News Bible*, published by the Bible Societies/Collins, © American Bible Society, New York, 1966, 1971, 1976.

First published 1998   ISBN 0-7197-0920-2   Printed in England

Teddy Horsley is a bear who likes to play hide and seek.

While Teddy Horsley covers his eyes,

Betsy Bear runs and finds somewhere to hide.

Teddy Horsley looks under the bed,
but Betsy Bear is not there.

Teddy Horsley looks in the wardrobe,
but Betsy Bear is not there.

Teddy Horsley looks behind the curtain,
but Betsy Bear is not there.

Teddy Horsley looks round the door,
but Betsy Bear is not there.

Teddy Horsley looks over the chair,
but Betsy Bear is not there.

Teddy Horsley looks beside the pot plant,
but Betsy Bear is not there.

However much Betsy Bear feels lost and alone,
she knows that
Teddy Horsley will go on seeking her.

Betsy Bear is a bear who likes to play
hide and seek.

While Betsy Bear covers her eyes,

Teddy Horsley runs and finds somewhere to hide.

Betsy Bear looks under the wheelbarrow,
but Teddy Horsley is not there.

Betsy Bear looks in the garden shed,
but Teddy Horsley is not there.

Betsy Bear looks behind the bushes,
but Teddy Horsley is not there.

Betsy Bear looks round the corner,
but Teddy Horsley is not there.

However much Teddy Horsley feels lost and alone,
he knows that Betsy Bear will go on seeking him.

Teddy Horsley and Betsy Bear
like to play hide and seek.

They hide under the table and in the cupboard.

They hide behind the wall and beside the tree.

However much Teddy Horsley and Betsy Bear
feel lost and alone,
they know that God will go on seeking them.

In *Hide and Seek*, Teddy Horsley and Betsy Bear's experience of playing hide and seek brings alive the message of Jesus' parables of the lost sheep and the lost coin in Luke 15:

So Jesus told them this parable:

'Suppose one of you has a hundred sheep and loses one of them - what does he do? He leaves the other ninety-nine sheep in the pasture and goes looking for the one that got lost until he finds it. When he finds it, he is so happy that he puts it on his shoulders and carries it back home. Then he calls his friends and neighbours together and says to them, "I am so happy I found my lost sheep. Let us celebrate!" In the same way, I tell you, there will be more joy in heaven over one sinner who repents than over ninety-nine respectable people who do not need to repent.

Or suppose a woman who has ten silver coins loses one of them - what does she do? She lights a lamp, sweeps her house, and looks carefully everywhere until she finds it. When she finds it, she calls her friends and neighbours together and says to them, "I am so happy I found the coin I lost. Let us celebrate!" In the same way, I tell you, the angels of God rejoice over one sinner who repents.'

The following questions suggest further ways of developing the links between the young child's experience, the story and the Bible passage.

Talk about playing hide and seek
  Who do you like to play hide and seek with?
  Where do you hide?
  Where do you look?
  How do you feel when you are hiding?
  How do you feel when you are seeking?
  Why do you like playing hide and seek?

Talk about the story
  Where did Teddy Horsley look for Betsy Bear?
  Where did Teddy Horsley find Betsy Bear?
  Where did Betsy Bear look for Teddy Horsley?
  Where did Betsy Bear find Teddy Horsley?
  How did they feel when they were hiding?
  How did they feel when they were found?

Talk some more about the story
  Where else might Teddy Horsley have looked for Betsy Bear?
  Where else might Betsy Bear have hidden?
  How would Teddy Horsley or Betsy Bear feel if they lost something

precious?
How would they feel when they found it again?

Think about the Bible passage
Where might the sheep have got lost?
How did the sheep feel when it got lost?
How did the shepherd feel when one sheep was lost?
Where did the shepherd go looking for the sheep?
How did the shepherd feel when he found it?
And how did the sheep feel?
Where might the woman have lost her precious coin?
How did the woman feel when she lost it?
How did she feel when she found it?
What did she do when she found the lost coin?
How does God feel when God finds someone who is lost?

Titles in the *Teddy Horsley* series:

Autumn	*Do and Tell*	*Explorer*
Good Morning	*Lights*	*Music Makers*
Neighbours	*Night Time*	*The Grumpy Day*
The Picnic	*The Present*	*The Song*
The Sunny Morning	*The Walk*	*The Windy Day*
Water		

Hardback *Teddy Horsley* books:
LARGE format books with LARGE words and pictures, each containing three stories

Out and About with Teddy Horsley:
 ❖ *The Walk*
 ❖ *Explorer*
 ❖ *Neighbours*

A Day with Teddy Horsley:
 ❖ *Good Morning*
 ❖ *The Grumpy Day*
 ❖ *Night Time*

Teddy Horsley Activity Pack:
 ❖ One *Teddy Horsley* book
 ❖ *Teddy Horsley* activity book
 ❖ *Teddy Horsley* picture card
 ❖ *Teddy Horsley* cotton tidybag
 ❖ Crayons
 ❖ Removable stickers